SUNDAY EXPRESS & DAILY EXPRESS
CARTOONS

Forty-third Series

AN EXPRESS BOOKS PUBLICATION

© 1989 Express Newspapers plc, Ludgate House, 245 Blackfriars Road, London SE1 9UX
Printed in Great Britain by Grosvenor Press (Portsmouth) Limited, England
Canadian Distributors: Copp Clark Pitman Ltd., 2775 Matheson Blvd East, Mississauga, Ontario, Canada, L4W 4P7 Tel: (416) 238 6074

Can. $7.95

FOREWORD

by

TIM RICE

Writer

&

Lyricist

Back in the early fifties I became an annual fan. By that I mean an Annual fan. Whether it was Eagle Annual or the Beano Book, Wisden or Ruff's Guide To The Turf, Old Moore or the Guinness Book Of Records, there was something about the yearly round-up in almost any field that I found irresistible. And one year in the Annuals shelves of Smith's in St. Albans I discovered Giles. Who was this genius with only one name who had come up with a goldmine of fun just in time for my Christmas stocking?

Every year since I have waited, not always in St. Albans, for the unmistakable shape and sparkle of the latest Giles collection to appear. Immediate purchase is essential and a wonderful investment, because one viewing of a Giles cartoon is never enough. There are always six or seven other comic ideas in every picture, in addition to the principal gag.

I no longer wonder what Giles' surname is, but I still wonder at his unstoppable flow of brilliance with word and line. He has seen off many rival annuals (though Wisden looks set to run a while yet) and is moving towards half a century of pre-eminence. In the world of theatre he would be Olivier and The Mousetrap combined, in his world it is enough to say he is Giles.

Tim Rice

"So far hooliganism isn't identified with Ascot. But any more language like you've just used on your jockey and it'll be on the way"

Daily Express, June 14th, 1988

"Explain to Senora that we have come here to escape from the British in Germany."

Daily Express, June 16th, 1988

"That 'Every Gardener's Handy Pruner' you gave dad for Father's Day—he's in the nick for carrying an offensive weapon."

Sunday Express, June 19th, 1988

"Don't let 'em soften you up, Mac—get in there and give the umpires hell"

Daily Express, June 21st, 1988

"Linda Kozlowski wouldn't have got Paul Hogan's millions if she'd said he looked a fair dinkum twit."

Daily Express, June 23rd, 1988

"When you come out you can tell me why you were parked for four hours outside the Wigmore Club on April the fifth, 1987"

Daily Express, June 28th, 1988

"Mamma—the gentleman wants to flog you a ticket for the Henley tea tent for a pony"

Daily Express, June 30th, 1988

'Even if we obey their chauvinist dress rules—it's still no women competitors at Henley'

Sunday Express, July 3rd, 1988

"She says—how she know we not English tourists in disguise?"

Daily Express, July 5th, 1988

"You can't hide yourself in there for ever because you're a member of the Test Selectors Board."

Daily Express, July 7th, 1988

'They're paying in gold bullion for six vanilla cornets and they want £24,997.60 change'

Sunday Express, July 10th, 1988

"Apart from two broken ribs, a cracked mandible, a fractured cuboid and two lovely black eyes, did he get a glimpse of Michael Jackson"

Daily Express, July 12th, 1988

"It's comforting to read that British women are blissfully happy with their husbands, and Geraldine—please knock it off while I'm taking my shot."

Daily Express, July 14th, 1988

'I always thought young Cowdrey was such a nice boy—I wonder what he did to deserve such a punishment'

Sunday Express, July 17th, 1988

"Stop pushing!"

Sunday Express, July 24th, 1988

"You call our swinging sixties rubbish—we could have bought Woburn for what you have to pay for a bed-sit."

Daily Express, July 26th, 1988

"She's going to run round the town to check if the others are cheaper before she pays."

Daily Express, July 28th, 1988

"I can't find a clause, should your holy matrimony 'bust' up, which would prevent your wife 'flogging' your story to the gutter press"

Sunday Express, July 31st, 1988

"Here we are, Ivy—Archbishopess of Canterbury!"

Daily Express, August 2nd, 1988   *(Headline: Anglican Church leaders allow women to become bishops.)*

"Can Her Majesty slip out for a quick half of bitter for her birthday?"

Daily Express, August 4th, 1988

"Go and tell daddy when he's finished wetting the coming Royal baby's head Mummy's got something to whisper in his ear."

Sunday Express, August 7th, 1988

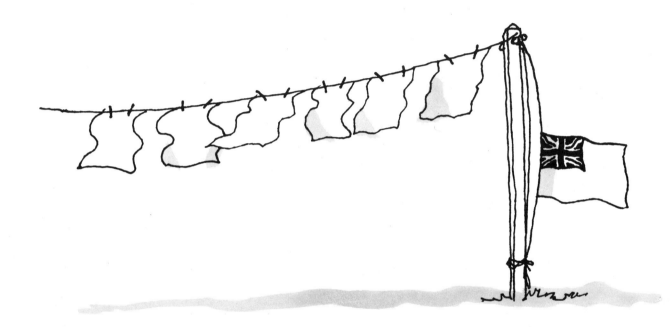

Birth of a baby.

"The Editor says he's not running 'The new fifth in line to the Throne looked like a stewed prune'."

Daily Express, August 9th, 1988

"It's worth a couple of barrels off the head gillie to get a couple of shots of the Royal baby's smile."

Sunday Express, August 14th, 1988

"Tell dad property prices are falling before he gets any further with his DIY extension"

Sunday Express, August 21st, 1988

"You mean we fixed our wedding on the same day as the first game of the season?"

Sunday Express, August 28th, 1988

"The lady says she's going to be a grandma and would you like a Downing Street job as an Advisory Executive?"

Sunday Express, September 4th, 1988

"I see you are not displaying the new poster we sent you, Mrs Williams"

Sunday Express, September 11th, 1988

"Tell your Grandma I'll have to think about asking the Lord to bring down an almighty power cut on the Olympic Games for the next two weeks"

Sunday Express, September 18th, 1988

"Nothing to do with the Olympic Games—they're in training to get back to work in the Daily Express next week"

(*Headline: The Family returned after a few weeks absence from the Express.*)   *Daily Express, September 22nd, 1988*

"To avoid some grievous bodily harm get Grandma out by the back door before she sees who's just come in."

Sunday Express, September 25th, 1988

"If we're all going to have Identity Cards, grandma can use the same one she had in 1939"

Daily Express, September 27th, 1988

"You should have called in the chemist and got a shot in the arm, bud"

Daily Express, September 29th, 1988

(Headline: Olympic runner failed drug test.)

"Richard didn't enjoy his game—every time he hit a ball Angela called STEROIDS!"

Sunday Express, October 2nd, 1988

"Don't think you're fooling ME."

"Don't get caught on the baby's age this time, dear—just say 'Under 21'."

(Headline: Fergie forgets Baby Bea's age.)

Daily Express, October 6th, 1988

"Very well, if you promise you're only slipping out to have your pictures taken by Lester Piggott and will all be back by bedtime . . ."

Daily Express, October 13th, 1988

"Give him a standing ovation — 5–0 down and he puts another one in our own goal."

(Headline: Mrs. Thatcher sets record for standing ovations.)

Sunday Express, October 16th, 1988

"You might pride yourself on scratching cars and knifing tyres but it takes brains to snap off six little trees"

Daily Express, October 18th, 1988   *(Headline: Vandals uproot hurricane damaged replacements.)*

"If you're planning on a new family car remember I shall be casting a vote"

Daily Express, October 20th, 1988

"Just try me with a free ticket to send him to Australia until he's forty"

Sunday Express, October 23rd, 1988

"It'll come back to him when he's been home for a bit"

Daily Express, October 25th, 1988

"I'm glad they haven't changed from miles to kilometres—Tom never quite mastered the change over to decimal coinage."

Daily Express, October 27th, 1988

"You have to call off your campaign to stop him building a new garage, or say goodbye to Uncle John's Victorian summer house."

Sunday Express, October 30th, 1988

"Achtung Herbie, here she comes again."

Daily Express, November 1st, 1988

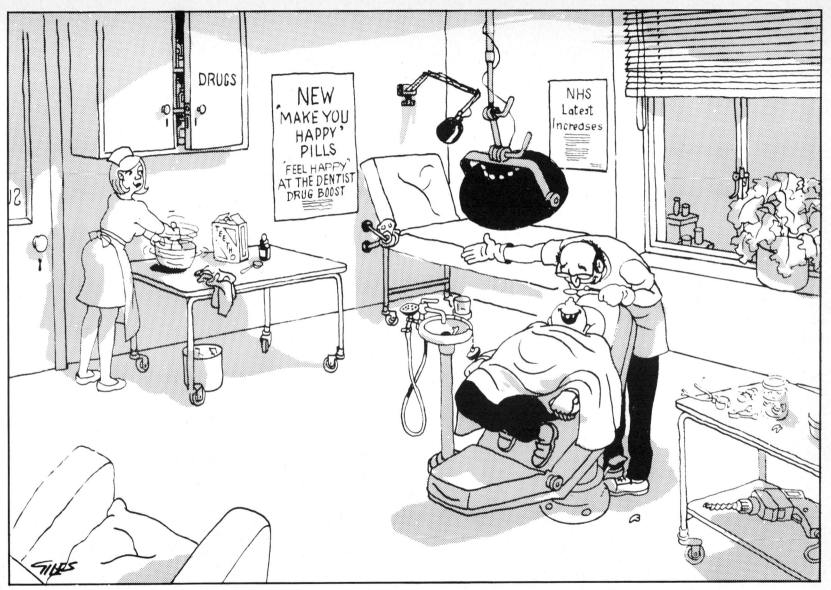

"Nurse, he'll need another couple of laughing pills—I think I've taken all the wrong ones out"

Daily Express, November 3rd, 1988

"Stand by for some real fireworks—Grandma's just found what's left of her hat you used on the guy"

Sunday Express, November 6th, 1988

"You've chained yourself to the wrong railings, duckie—the Chancellor lives next door."

Daily Express, November 8th, 1988

"Look who's asking me why I don't take a page out of La Belle Diana's book!"

Daily Express, November 10th, 1988

"You realise that Prince Charles and the rest of your Guard of Honour went back on Friday."

Sunday Express, November 13th, 1988

"We know you're entitled to voice your opinion on the nurses' strike—but not out loud."

Daily Express, November 15th, 1988

"How many times must I tell you: 'Is not Noddy the most stupid ...... you ever saw? 'NOT' Aint Noddy the most stupid ...... you ever saw?'"

Daily Express, November 17th, 1988

"The BBC wants to verify the Children in Need bid for tickets to Disneyland at £2,000 a head."

Sunday Express, November 20th, 1988

"It's from Gorbachev—he can't visit the Queen because we chopped Charles the First's head off in 1649."

(Headline: Thatcher tells Queen cancel Russian visit because of Tsarist executions.) Daily Express, November 22nd, 1988

"And hold your tongue about NUPE or it'll be me humping you all the way to the ward."

Daily Express, November 24th, 1988

"We sympathise that you have six prodigies to bring into the world before you resign, but overtaking in this fog is motorway madness."

Sunday Express, November 27th, 1988

"We sold out of Father Christmases by the end of August—can we interest him in Hanging Judges?"

Daily Express, December 1st, 1988

"You think your judge should be fired and you demand to see your lawyer? No problem—they're both in the same cell-block as you."

Sunday Express, December 4th, 1988

"If Currie means it's going to save me this morning trip to collect one egg out of you bunch of layabouts then hooray for salmonella."

Daily Express, December 6th, 1988

"On your feetskis, it's not the Queen of England, it's bloody Jean Rookski."

Daily Express, December 8th, 1988

"Stand by for tidings of good cheer from the neighbours—Dad's just blown every fuse in the road."

Sunday Express, December 11th, 1988

"Like the Princess said, luv, you don't have to love children."

Daily Express, December 13th, 1988

"We're all right for eggs—a man called and sold Vera 24,000 at a penny each"

Daily Express, December 15th, 1988

"He's not to have those till Christmas—back where you found them!"

Sunday Express, December 18th, 1988

"Dad says the Germans have got it right banning Forces Christmas parties in Germany—he says he's for banning Christmas parties everywhere."

Daily Express, December 20th, 1988

"I haven't read anything about farmers altering their chickens' diet."

Daily Express, December 22nd, 1988

"Thanks for coming Uncle Jolyon and thanks for buying the children that lovely organ."

Daily Express, December 27th, 1988

"I read about Dr. Runcie and his crush on a little Church girl, but you're not using *me* as a stepping-stone to become Archbishop of Canterbury."

Daily Express, December 29th, 1988

"Five, bull, double top, or bang goes your chance of a Knighthood."

Sunday Express, January 1st, 1989

(Headline: Champion dart player gets MBE.)

"Wakey, wakey—the lady's little boys can't get their Garfield and Odie suits off."

(Headline: 'Junior Doctors' overworked say Junior Doctors.)

Daily Express, January 3rd, 1989

"All Bows of Burning Gold, Arrows of Desire, Spears, Swords, etc, will be placed on my desk at the front of the hall."

Daily Express, January 5th, 1989

"It'll be extremely bad for your health if she hears you say 'Morning Fatso'"

Sunday Express, January 8th, 1989

"You've upset grandpa asking him if he wore a black armband for Hitler or Mussolini."

Daily Express, January 12th, 1989

"As you don't trust him and I don't trust any of yer, I brought my friend Rasputin Mataharivich who's done a bit of flying"

(Headline: Heathrow security shambles.)

Sunday Express, January 15th, 1989

'Don't you let me open my papers and see you ski-ing about in Klosters'

Daily Express, January 17th, 1989

'That's not very nice, Angus—if he doesn't give you a pass you'll be back before half-time to bust his head in.'

Daily Express, January 19th, 1989

"I don't mind you kissing Mandy Rowbotham, but if I catch you kissing Brian Clough . . ."

Sunday Express, January 22nd, 1989

"Under these new laws, for not getting him off fourteen charges of robbery with violence, he reckons you owe him."

Daily Express, January 24th, 1989

"These TV Soap boozers Princess Diana complains about—we could do with a few round here."

Daily Express, January 26th, 1989

"One station nearer to Auntie Ivy's for tea and he threatens he'll call the Guardian Angels."

Sunday Express, January 29th, 1989

'Whatever they put in their new Secret White paper it will still include our usual two-hour wait.'

Daily Express, January 31st, 1989

"Remember me? I got three years for helping you with your enquiries."

(Headline: Police replace prison officers.)

Daily Express, February 2nd, 1989

"This'll take her mind off the chat line bill—they've managed to get hold of a TV satellite dish"

My grandfather can remember when the Bengal Lancers used the Afghans for rifle practice for well over a century

Daily Express, February 7th, 1989

"Knock off this clean up Britain Mum—they've already labelled us the most anti-social snobs in the avenue."

Daily Express, February 9th, 1989

"How the hell do I know what bacteria is in it—we've got one hour to get to Crufts—eat!"

Sunday Express, February 12th, 1989

"There aren't twenty-one people who'd send Dad a Valentine card—he sent them to himself."

Daily Express, February 14th, 1989

First snow

Daily Express, February 16th, 1989

"Over here, Fireworks—they're paying me an extra sixpence to keep you in fitness and in health."

Sunday Express, February 19th, 1989

"You are all very fortunate that you live in a country with less stringent laws about literature than Iran."

(Headline: A writer was sentenced to death for upsetting Iranians.)   *Daily Express, February 21st, 1989*

"I think it's their Jean Rook—I've never seen a Geisha Girl throw Zukiahso overhead in one."

Daily Express, February 23rd, 1989

(Headline: Jean Rook visits Japan.)

"Take Dad a cup of tea and tell him who won the fight"

'Message from Supreme HQ, M'Lord—owing to increased charges by Water Privatisation M'Lady says all manoeuvres will be cut by one hour.'

Daily Express, February 28th, 1989

"'We are a Grandmother', but I don't think 'we' are amused."

(Headline: Mrs. Thatcher announces "We are a Grandmother".)

Sunday Express, March 5th, 1989

"I didn't say his after-lunch cigars cause a hole in the ozone, I simply said they can't help."

Daily Express, March 7th, 1989

"Doctor won't be very happy if that's one of those Red-Nose jokes."

(Headline: Zany fun for Red Nose Day March 10th.)

Daily Express, March 9th, 1989

"It's no good—it won't come off and he's on in ten minutes."

Sunday Express, March 12th, 1989

"Failing to tell Judge Pickles why you refuse to wear your new shoes could land you in prison for a very long time."

(Headline: Girl jailed for refusing to give evidence.)

Daily Express, March 14th, 1989

"I'd like to take advantage of earning a bit on the side—just light cleaning and tea-making, of course."

Daily Express, March 16th, 1989

(Headline: Call girl claims 'I worked at the House of Commons'.)

"Haven't you read that doctors are free to advertise, Hilary?"

Sunday Express, March 19th, 1989

"I remember you belting off to beat me to the phone in Christine Keeler's days!"

Daily Express, March 21st, 1989

"If you've never met this Christine Keeler why the nervous rush to the phone every time it rings?"

Sunday Express, June 9th, 1963

"This isn't Dad—it's a straw-packed dummy!"

Sunday Express, March 26th, 1989

"Won't make a lotter difference to Harry who owns the pubs—he ain't bought a drink since they disbanded the Home Guard."

Daily Express, March 25th, 1989

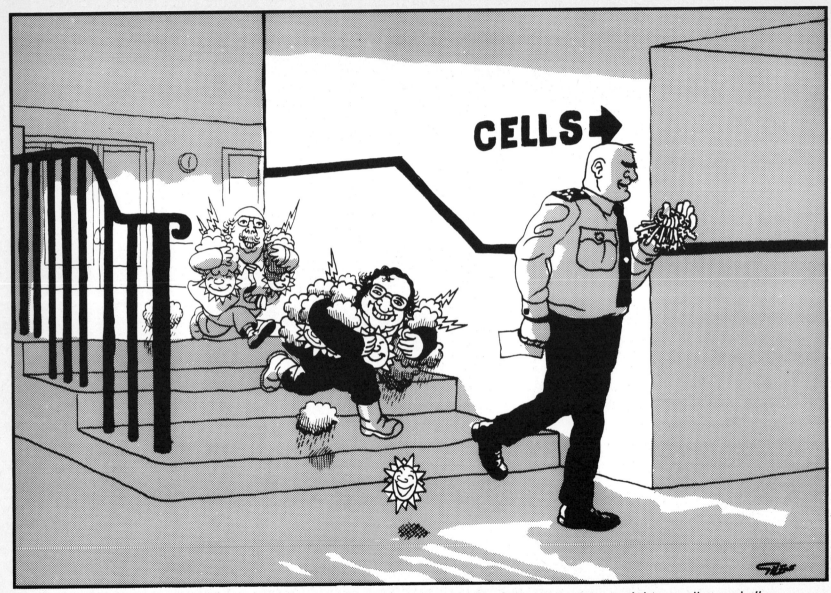

"If you're coming to us for protection every time you get your weather forecast wrong you might as well move in."

Daily Express, March 28th, 1989

"My brother Eddie says he's never had much confidence in you since the start."

(Headline: Police: Polls show drop in confidence.)

Daily Express, March 30th, 1989

"One of them behind the seat should shift 'em before the John Wayne film starts."

Sunday Express, April 2nd, 1989

(Headline: Explosives found behind seat on aircraft.)

"Any excuse for ten minutes lay-in. Today his mind is troubled about who owns Harrods."

Daily Express, April 4th, 1989

"You've missed him. If you hurry you might catch him before he leaves Downing Street"

Daily Express, April 6th, 1989

"I know they love Gorbachev but I'm not having vodka and balalaika all day"

Sunday Express, April 9th, 1989

"I like the smart uniform they're wearing to make their 'Really good start on the lawn this Sunday'"

Sunday Express, April 16th, 1989

"What's it to be—two tickets for Sinatra or Aspects of Love, or pay off the mortgage?"

Daily Express, April 20th, 1989

"Where you went wrong is you should've turned right when you came out of West India Dock Road."

Sunday Express, April 23rd, 1989

"Watch your step, my boy, if you don't want to get caught with a £60m palimony lawsuit like Clint Eastwood"

Sunday Express, April 30th, 1989

"He won't mind—he laughed his head off at the pictures of Prince William doing it"

Sunday Express, May 7th, 1989   (Headline: Cameras catch Prince William pinching Games Mistress's bottom.)

"Well, that's skateboards out as an alternative means of getting him to work."

Sunday Express, May 14th, 1989

"Margaret, I think you are overdoing this Eternal Youth Electrical Bath treatment."

Sunday Express, May 21st, 1989

"Cut out *'Mrs Ringboan singing Jerusalem sounded like one of Joe Barney's cows having a calf.'* You can't afford £600,000 libel damages."

(Headline: Private Eye fined £600,000 libel damages.)

Sunday Express, May 28th, 1989

"I bet she didn't know her umbrella handle was made of ivory"

Sunday Express, June 4th, 1989

"We could put six in the sitting room, four in with Grandma, three with Vera . . ."

"Why should I let him win as it's Father's day? Check Mate!"

Sunday Express, June 18th, 1989

"I think Her Ladyship has allocated the household transport for Wimbledon, M'Lord."

Sunday Express, June 25th, 1989

"Dad's been listening to too much McEnroe <u>and</u> Prince Charles."

The Sunday Express, July 2nd, 1989

"Like me to fill it in for you?"

The Sunday Express, July 9th, 1989

"Before we start the holidays we're all going to sign a little form declaring we all pay our own litter fines."

The Sunday Express, July 23rd, 1989